This heartfelt story is dedicated to my loving family. Written in memory of my Mom and Dad. ~~ Thank you both for your beautiful spirits.
-DB

For Mom and Dad
-GA

Summary: It's Cecily Jane's first day walking home from school. But when she meets Mr. Crow, she discovers all sorts of connections in this unusual book about loss, family and spirit.

Clear Fork Publishing www.clearforkpublishing.com
P.O. Box 870 102 S. Swenson Stamford, Texas 79553 (325)773-5550

Printed and Bound in the United States of America.
ISBN - 978-1-946101-70-9
LCN - 2018947256

CROW
SPIRIT

written by **Debra Bartsch**
illustrated by **Gael Abary**

HappyReading ♡
Deb Bartsch

Grandma always said
crows are like a big family,
they watch out for their own.

Today I felt like I was part of the family.

I was walking home from school by myself for the first time and I was a bit scared.

I stood at the crosswalk,
and there
on the other side of the street
was a CROW!

I saw him there,
just like he was waiting for me.

I'm sure he nodded when the light changed, and then
when I crossed, he walked along in front of me a bit
– kind of strutting as he walked.

You know, how they go, his head cocking from side to side opposite of his body, so I wasn't so scared anymore.

I said, "Hello, Mr. Crow."
And you know what, he said?
He said,

"CAAWW
CAAWW"

back to me!

When I got home
I was so proud of myself
and amazed by that big old crow.
I ran inside and told Mama about it.

I reminded her about what Gram used to
say about crows living together
in big nests high up in the trees,
all helping each other out.
Mama smiled.

"Wish Gram and Grandpop were still here.
I sure miss them both." Then Mama said, "Come on,
Sugar, let's go into the kitchen and make a snack.
I'll tell you more about crows. And yes, I miss them too."

Mama sliced some juicy peaches and blueberries, and passed a snickerdoodle cookie, just like Gram used to make.

"Your Grandma always had a special connection with those birds," Mama said.

"Gram loved how smart crows
are and how when the parents
hunted food for their babies,
aunt and uncle crows
would watch out
for the little fledglings
still in the nest."

She told me how when she was my age,
Gram would take her out in the
backyard and point up at that old tree
like she wanted to go up there
along with them, you know,
join them or something.

She talked to Grandpop about it a lot.

He'd smile and agree.

"Yes dear, they are smart,
watching out for each other
like we watch over ours."

Mama talked about how
she and Grandma and Grandpop
would watch crows in the backyard,
strutting and chatting together.

"It's just like when people
get together and have a picnic,
same thing, just crows being social.

They'd listen to those crows calling to each
other from treetop to treetop, warning of
intruders, very protective of the young.

"Your Gram believed in crows,

she felt their spirit like a family spirit."

"Mama, do you feel that
same connection?"
Mama nodded yes
and I did too.

Mama took my hand
and walked me out
to that same old tree.
There was Mr. Crow.
I'd recognize him anywhere.

"Sure hope he walks me to school tomorrow.
Mr. Crow and I have a lot to talk about."

I lifted up my arms and sang,

CAW
CAW
CAW

Mr. Crow called right back.

CAWW
CAWW
CAWW
CAWW

I could almost see Grandma
and Grandpop smiling.

Fun facts about Crows

Crows are very large intelligent black birds. There are over 40 species of Crows.

Crow's nests can be made of sticks built in trees, with layers of mud and layers of soft fur, feathers, string, or hair.

Three to six eggs are laid between April and May. The nesting eggs need about 18 days of sitting time. A nest can also be built on ledges of buildings.

Fledglings are young, juvenile crows. Fledglings stay in the nest for up to 35 days. Once they are on the ground they try to "get their wings" and might look a bit wonky in learning to fly but rest assured the grown up crows are keeping a close eye on them.

Roosts are sleeping areas. Crows are social birds that live together, sometimes roosting on the branches of an entire tree.

Crows are omnivores, meaning they'll eat just about anything; vegetables, fruit, insects, other birds and rodents.

The Migratory Bird Act of 1918 protects certain birds. It is illegal to harm or hurt a crow.

Spirit can mean energy, soul, life. Some people believe all living things have a spirit. In this story, I've tried to show how birds, like crows, can possibly carry the spirit of loved ones who've passed on.

If a crow is bothering you, try to realize he is more than likely watching out for his young, and you might just be in his way! So, give these intelligent family birds another look, they just might be helping you out in your future!

The Audubon Society of Portland is a great resource for more information on these wonderful birds: https://audubonportland.org/

Deb Bartsch writes from a kid's-eye view of the world. From fun-filled adventures raising her family in the country to daily inspiration with laughing grandkids, life is full of sunshine and rain, plus a few mud puddles.

Deb wrote her debut story from the home in Portland, Oregon where she grew up - a house filled with stories, laughter, faith, and music. With her library card and Bookmobile visits, by age 5 she knew someday, she would just have to write those beautiful books for kids too. She is so thankful that someday, is here.

www.debbartschillustration.com

Gael Abary has loved drawing since she was a child. She spent many years in NYC working as an illustrator and metalsmith before moving to Woodstock, NY, where her daughter was born. Through reading with her little one, she developed a passion for picture books. This is her debut as a children's book illustrator.

Say hello at gaelabary.com.

Gram's Snickerdoodle Recipe

Ingredients:

3/4 cup butter
1/4 cup shortening
1 3/4 cups sugar
2 eggs
1 teaspoon vanilla extract

1 teaspoon baking soda
1 teaspoon cream of tartar
1/4 teaspoon salt
2 3/4 cups all-purpose flour
4 tablespoons sugar
2 teaspoons cinnamon

Directions:

Preheat oven to 375 degrees.
Cream together butter, shortening, and 1 3/4 cups sugar until light and fluffy.
Blend in eggs and vanilla. Combine baking soda, cream of tartar, salt, and flour,
and stir into creamed butter-sugar mixture, mix until blended.
If cookie dough is sticky, add 1 or 2 tablespoons flour.
Chill for about an hour. Mix the 4 tablespoons sugar and the cinnamon.
Spoon and roll cookie dough into 1 inch balls, then roll in cinnamon-sugar mixture.
Place cinnamon-sugar covered balls on cookie sheet. 12 at a time.
Bake at 375° for 10-12 minutes until lightly golden and your kitchen smells delicious.
Cool 1 minute, then move cookies on to cookie rack and cool. Yummy!
Serve with love and a smile!

CPSIA information can be obtained
at www.ICGtesting.com
Printed in the USA
BVHW020544070319
541777BV00005B/6/P

9 781946 101709